WHAT WORKS WHEN MEMORY STOPS WORKING

WHAT WORKS WHEN MEMORY STOPS WORKING

Charting A Course

KARIN W. ERICSON

Onion River Press

Onion River Press
191 Bank Street
Burlington, VT 05401

ISBN: 978-1-949066-75-3
Library of Congress Control Number: 2021907096

Publisher's Cataloging-in-Publication Data
Names: Ericson, Karin W., author.
Title: What works when memory stops working : charting a course / Karin W. Ericson.
Description: Burlington, VT: Onion River Press, 2021.
Identifiers: LCCN: 2021907096 | ISBN: 978-1-949066-75-3
Subjects: LCSH Ericson, Karin W.--Family. | Alzheimer's disease--Patients--Biography. | Mothers and daughters. | BISAC BIOGRAPHY & AUTOBIOGRAPHY / Personal Memoirs | FAMILY & RELATIONSHIPS / Eldercare | HEALTH & FITNESS / Diseases / Alzheimer's & Dementia
Classification: LCC RC523.2 .E75 2021 | DDC 616.8/31/092--dc23

Dedicated to my father, Ralph White,
whose love made this journey happier for
my mother.

Contents

MY MOTHER'S MEMORY

My mother's memory disappeared

a piece at a time

like the embezzler

who took a coin each day

so no one would notice

until the account

was empty.

Poem by Karin W. Ericson

I

Introduction

My father, Ralph White, and my mother, Shirley Christie, were high school sweethearts. Dad was a star on the football team that won the 1943 high school state championship in Westboro, Massachusetts. He was a top student and, although he had lots of friends, was shy. Mom was the popular one with a laugh that could be heard above others. She was known to get on stage during school dances and sing with the band. Dad can still recall hearing her sing "Moonlight Becomes You" in perfect pitch.

Dad was given a football scholarship to Columbia and played his Freshman year until enlisting in the Army and becoming an officer. Following his service, they married in 1947. Dad re-enrolled in Columbia and continued playing football and earning high grades in the School of Engineering. Mom worked in the registrar's office at Columbia and later worked part-time at a nursery school.

Fast forward through births of children and grandchildren, job promotions, trips to Europe, and ski adventures to the realization that something was changing with Mom.

In helping my mother as she slid into Alzheimer's Disease, our family stumbled and fell many times. Logic told us to respond to questions in a certain way, and logic was often wrong. For instance, when she told me her parents were going to be worried about her when she didn't come home, I quietly told her, "Oh, Mom, your parents passed away years ago." She cried and said, "No one told me they died! I didn't get to go their funerals or say good-bye." We realized we needed a different approach. A different approach to everything.

Writing these essays, I recognized that much of life is circular. The lessons my mother helped me learn as a child and teenager served me in helping her through the many stages of her disease. As Mom's memory failed more and more, I was able to fill in the blanks for her and guide her through the challenges and fears that confronted her.

Here are some of the lessons I learned in our journey as a family. Memoir and self-help are woven together in these stories of our lives before the disease took hold, through Mom's failing memory as years passed, and finally of her dying. May our learnings shed some light on the path into and through what is often a dark territory, give you some hope, and ease your journey.

2

Holidays and Signposts

Traditions Made, Broken and Recreated

As adults, the only thing I remember that my mother and I disagreed about was how to celebrate Christmas. Actually, she didn't know we disagreed because for years I did not tell her how I envisioned Christmas for my family. It's not that on a daily basis I am weak and unable to state my opinions. In fact, I usually state my opinions even when I'm not asked for them — something I'm working on — but when I first discussed having Christmas at my house when Dave and I had young children, my mother said, "Christmas isn't Christmas unless it is at 70 Woodland Road." Yes, that is my parents' address in North Hampton, New Hampshire. Not mine.

What could I say? I had no traditions. I wanted them. I wanted Christmas in my own home, I wanted my children to be at their home for Christmas.

I said, "Okay." And for years and with two children, we

schlepped our presents and ourselves from our homes to theirs. Don't get me wrong. For many years it was fun. My brother and his wife and two children were pressured to come to 70 Woodland Road, also, and we had lots of fun eating, drinking, and sharing old traditions. I silently bemoaned that I had no traditions, but we were having fun just the same.

On Christmas Eve we had dinner sitting around my parents' large cherry dining room table, resplendent with white tablecloth, Mom's best china and silverware, and red candles lined down the center, each at a different height in an oh-so-artsy fashion. There was a fire in the fireplace, and Christmas carols played in the background. Dinner was served buffet style on the sideboard —filet mignon, potatoes, cauliflower casserole, steaming hot dinner rolls.

The year I proclaimed my vegetarianism created a stir that not even a mouse could have missed.

"I made fettucine with chicken for you, Karin," Mom said.

"I don't eat chicken, Mom."

"Well, just pick out the chicken then."

"I don't eat anything that is cooked with meat in the same casserole."

"I didn't think chicken was meat."

I decided not to say I didn't eat things that once had faces. That the "juice" from the filet mignon was not juice. Not exactly Christmas talk. Best not to go there as people were sopping it up with their dinner rolls.

I had cauliflower casserole and potatoes, and both the rolls and I were steaming.

Our family was inclined to give many small presents so the space under the tree was filled and spilled onto the surrounding floor space. We are a generous lot, so we spent a lot of time wrapping ahead of time and unwrapping on Christmas. My parents were especially generous. Mom proclaimed every year as we walked through the obstacle course of packages, "Oh, it's just a small Christmas!" We all laughed, grateful that Christmas was as abundant as always.

One Christmas Eve, just before dinner was served, Mom announced she wanted all the presents opened that night.

"You can save the ones from you to your children until Christmas morning if you like, but I'd like all the other presents opened tonight." She had never been able to see my niece and nephew open their presents because my brother's family went to the other grandparents late on Christmas Eve and stayed there for Christmas morning. Mom wanted to see Brian and Andrea open their presents.

I understood her position. "Okay, Mom, but my kids can open theirs from you tomorrow morning like always."

"No, they can open them tonight. I don't want them sitting watching Brian and Andrea open their presents."

"They won't mind," I said. "They'll understand."

"I mind. I don't want to do it that way. Why are you creating a conflict on Christmas Eve? If we're at my house, we can do it my way, and this is how I'd like to do it."

"Well, they're my children, and I want them to open them tomorrow like always," I said, pulling courage from some deep recesses of my personality. Well, not exactly, but I never spoke that way to my mother.

I got the look. Squinted eyes, head down looking over the top of her glasses. Jaw clenched. A quick snort. A sharp exhale of breath. Arms crossed over her chest.

This was the look that as a small child melted me into a pool of emotion, caused me to trail behind my mother clutching at her pant legs, asking for forgiveness, groveling.

The timer on the stove dinged, the heat kicked on sending slow trickles of water into radiators, the dog rolled over and snored. These sounds only broke the silence of the room and the snapshot of The Look. I stood my ground on shaking legs.

Mom harrumphed and turned on her heel to take the casserole out of the oven.

After dinner, I found my father. Having witnessed the earlier scene between my mother and me, he had wisely retreated to the television room.

"I need your help," I said. Then the tears came. "I have no traditions, Dad. All the traditions are Mom's. I never have Christmas at my house. My children never wake up in their own beds for Christmas. Heck, we don't even have a Christmas tree here anymore. Mom decorates the ficus tree with clip-on cardinals and silver balls. I want my children to open their presents on Christmas Day, not on Christmas Eve. I want a Christmas tree with all the ornaments I've collected for years."

I couldn't stop, stuck in the mode I call "And Another Thing." It's how I got when my emotions were out of control and I layered on every upset I'd ever suffered, often sewing conflicts together with the thinnest of threads. Christmas upsets could be linked to Easter and 4th of July with the holiday thread, incidents that took place years ago brought into the present.

"And another thing," I said, "My children never got to be in a Christmas pageant and dress up like angels or shepherds.

I never got to sew costumes. I really want to have Christmas at our house next year. Can you please talk to Mom about all this?"

Mouth agape, Dad nodded and said, "Okay, I'll work on it. I think we'll need to do the presents tonight and work on the other plan for next year. "

"Okay," I conceded, "but my children are opening their presents from Dave and me tomorrow morning, not tonight."

Dad brokered the Christmas deal. We never talked about the Christmas Eve conflict again. Mom and Dad just announced they would come to Vermont from then on. The following year, Mom and Dad drove to our house, presents crammed into their car.

We established new traditions. We attended midnight service at our church, where they heard me sing in the choir. We sang Christmas carols around our player piano with a fire burning in the fireplace of our 1843 brick home, lights twinkling amidst greenery on the mantle. The Christmas ornaments I had collected for years hung on a fragrant tree. I did my best to create memories and traditions of our own that would last.

But ours was not the perfect Christmas card photo experience. Mom was starting to struggle with memory loss and confusion, though my family and I were not aware. Dad kept us insulated from all he was going through, and I failed to notice any signposts until Mom forgot my birthday.

My birthday, December 18, came and went without a call or a present. On December 19, I was tempted to call my parents and see if I could prompt an, "Oh, my goodness, I lost track of the day! Happy birthday! I am so sorry I didn't call yesterday." Instead, I crossed my arms and complained to my husband that my parents forgot about my birthday for the first time in 48 years.

In a few days, my parents would be driving to our home for another Christmas. I was sure they would remember before they arrived. But when December 24 came and there was still no acknowledgment of my birthday, I made plans to tell my parents how upset I was.

Dave suggested I let it go.

"Let it go? My parents didn't call me on my birthday. I don't blame my father. He is not likely to remember. It's my mother who keeps track of these things. It's almost a week past my birthday, and they've said nothing. They forgot my birthday!"

We went to dinner at a restaurant on the lake in North Hero, Vermont, sharing a lovely solarium with other families who didn't want to cook. The conversation was happy and lively with no mention of my birthday. Also, no birthday presents. No raising a glass to my health. I wanted to say something but how could I without seeming selfish?

On the way home, we all remarked how lovely the dinner had been and how nice it was to all be together. I waited for my opening. My mother asked if we went to that restaurant often.

"No, we usually go to Blue Paddle. We went there for my birthday last week." That would get them, I thought. My birthday *last* week. The car was silent.

Finally, my mother said in a small voice, "We remembered your birthday."

"Well, actually," I said, friendlier than I had been feeling a minute earlier, "you didn't."

What the heck was I thinking, mentioning my missed birthday on Christmas Eve? I wished for a do-over. I pictured a different scenario, pictured not telling them they missed my birthday. Pictured reaching back and taking my mother's hand and saying, "I love you Mom. I'm so glad you're here for Christmas." Instead, my declaration stuck to all of us like frost on windowpanes.

We drove the five miles home in silence. What could I say? I kept parting my lips to speak, but nothing came out.

When we arrived home and hung up our coats, my mother came to me with a pained look on her face. "Oh Karin, I'm so sorry we forgot your birthday. I feel terrible. We've never forgotten your birthday. Ever."

"It's fine, Mom," I said, "I shouldn't have said anything. I'm so glad you're here." I hugged her and cursed my selfishness.

That next day, Christmas, my parents gave me three sweaters: one emerald green and two periwinkle blue that were exactly alike. Exactly.

"She liked the sweater so much," Dad joked, "that she gave you two of them!" Everyone laughed, including Mom.

"I think one of those was for Cindy," Mom said, referring to my brother's wife. "Oops! I wonder if she got two of something also!"

As everyone opened mountains of presents from my parents, I sat without any boxes other than the identical blue sweaters and the electric green one.

"Where are the rest of your presents, Karin?" Mom asked.

"I think these are the ones I have," I said, trying to sound pleasant and grateful, still thinking the green sweater could only be worn on St. Patrick's Day. What was she thinking? Where were my Christmas presents? Where were my birthday presents, damn it?

"Oh, no, I had lots more for you," Mom said. "Ralph, did you get all the presents from the third floor? I'm sure they must be there. I'll mail them as soon as we get back. I was just in too much of a hurry packing. I'm so sorry!"

It was really okay that I didn't have more presents. They would arrive next week, and I'd have Christmas all over again. I had to smile — the scene was lovely chaos — everyone happily opening presents, paper strewn on the floor or balled up and thrown into large black trash bags like we were playing basketball. Dad tried on clothes and pretended to ski in them, like he did every year when he received clothing. We all laughed when he tried on a bathrobe and mimicked skiing motions.

Our daughter was home from college. Our son was in from DC, his future wife also spending the holidays with us. Our dog Bentley slept in front of the big fireplace; the cats curled up nearby. The turkey was cooking in the kitchen and all the aromas, the ones that reminded me of family, wafted into the living room. Norman Rockwell happily meeting our family.

On December 26, when my parents arrived home from the holidays, Dad called and told me they looked all over the house and there weren't any more presents for me. They would send me a check for Christmas. And for my birthday.

It took the year until my next birthday, when Dad called, and finally until Christmas for me to realize that the missed birthday, two periwinkle blue sweaters and the St. Patrick's Day green one, had been signs of Mom's Alzheimer's.

After that Christmas, I noticed when we were together that Mom asked me the same question over and over; told me the same story three times; asked if she could set the table for me when she had just finished setting it.

Mom was diagnosed with Alzheimer's the next fall, but we never spoke of it, never uttered the name of the disease. It was as if we naively thought if we didn't name it, it didn't exist.

The following year, after a four-hour drive from New Hampshire on December 24, Mom and Dad arrived and carried in bags of presents. Mom took off her coat, sat down and announced, "I'm ready to go. It was a nice visit, but I need to get home."

"We just got here, Shirl," Dad said.

"No, we've been here forever. I'm ready to go. Let's go."

"It's Christmas Eve. Everyone is here. Karin and Dave's house is decorated for Christmas. Doesn't it look great?"

"Yes, it looks great," she said, "but I want to go home."

We convinced Mom to stay overnight with the help of some calming medication. The next day, we opened presents. Our midday supper was rushed but fun with Christmas poppers and paper hats, another tradition we'd started. I was so tradition-starved that nearly everything that was repeated for two years became tradition. Christmas cookie baking as a family — tradition! Walk along the lake — tradition! Open presents for the dog and cats — tradition!

By 2:00 pm on Christmas Day, we had staved off Mom's anxiety as long as we could. She started talking about going home as soon as she woke up, and we had run out of things that forced her to stay. Dinner was over. Presents were over. We had walked along the lake.

"I think we'll head home," Dad said, and we all knew it was time.

And I knew it was the last time we'd all have Christmas at our house. Mom needed to be in familiar settings, with her comfortable bed, her plates, her napkins, her kitchen. I'd do all the cooking, but at her house, where she was comfortable.

Two years later, Mom moved into an Alzheimer's facility. From then on, we brought Christmas to her.

* * *

What works:

- Consulting a physician if there are memory issues or changes in interactions develop with your loved one so any medications that can help get started as soon as possible.
- Asking the person closest to the one with symptoms if everything is all right. We were afraid to ask Dad. When we finally did, he seemed relieved. He was hoping Mom's memory issues weren't noticeable, but he was living the challenges every day. Once we mentioned it, he had someone to talk to. It allowed us to plan strategies to help Mom.
- If you miss a signpost, it's all right. We all have a little denial affecting us. Forgive yourself.
- Remembering that none of us is perfect. We all make mistakes. Hopefully, we learn and move forward. It's easy to become frustrated and speak harshly. Resolve

to be more patient the next time. It's often harder on the person losing their memory than it is on family or friends.

3

One for the Road

Driving Lessons

Mom teaches me to drive in a 1966 Ford Fairlane, dark green. The top is a fake convertible, textured like canvas. My mother is the chosen driving teacher, although I don't remember choosing her. Mom sits in the middle of the bench seat as if cuddling close to me. But that's not why she is on my side of the car. She wants to be able to smash on the brake if I get into trouble, and her hand is suspended in the air in case she has to grab the wheel and yank me back onto the road. Not a lot of trust.

Mom is a good driver. She never exceeds the speed limit, makes full stops at stop signs, yields when she is supposed to. She teaches me to use hand turn signals, though I know we have signal lights that can be activated from the lever next to the steering column. So, I have to stick my left arm straight out for a left turn, arm bent at a 90-degree angle, hand pointing to the sky for a right turn. It is embarrassing. Mom constantly glances from road to rear view mirror to side mirror to road signs, hypervigilant for any potential crisis — a car careening out of control ready to smash us from behind; balls or children, dogs or cats ready to rush into our path; or sneaky signs heralding school and hospital zones. On top of it all, there are fire engines to stay 500 feet behind, crosswalks and hydrants to park far away from, and meters to be fed nickels and dimes. It's a jungle out there!

I take driver's education from the calm teachers at Winnacunnet High School in Hampton, New Hampshire, in a car with its own special emergency foot brake on the instructor's side of the car. I prefer the driver's ed teacher who is, relative to Mom, relaxed. After all, this is his chosen profession, which requires him to have nerves of steel, unending patience, and kind words for his terrified students. Perhaps I am a slow study. One day I inadvertently put my foot on the gas instead of the brake as we careened around a corner and nearly drove through a bakery.

Mr. Driver's Ed yells at me, "You almost drove right into the bakery! I said put on the brakes and you put on the gas!"

Mom resumes, giving me practice sessions between classes.

One day we drive on the road from North Hampton to Hampton, a moderately traveled road with nice houses on each side bordered by stone walls that stop rolling balls and small children. As we pass one neighborhood, I see Miss Ball, my physical education teacher, raking leaves. She must wonder if we are a one-car funeral procession. Mom never lets me drive even the 35-mph speed limit, so we crawl everywhere.

Miss Ball waves. I do not wave back. I have to keep my hands on the 10 o'clock – 2 o'clock hand positions.

The next day I see Miss Ball. "You looked like you were scared stiff when you were driving," she says in our packed PE class. "Who was that sitting so close to you?"

"Not a boyfriend," offers one of the popular girls in school.

When I see Miss Ball at our 25-year class reunion I remind her of the conversation. She has no idea what I am talking about.

In August of Mom's third year with Alzheimer's, her friends told my father they saw Mom running stop signs and ignoring yield signs. One day, Dad and Mom, having left the house in separate cars, arrived side-by-side at a major intersection. Mom rolled down her window to ask Dad a question. Dad waved her into his lane. Mom had been in the lane for oncoming vehicles with no awareness of her error. Luckily, no one had turned into the lane, but that incident, coupled with reports from friends, made Dad realize Mom's driving days needed to end. This was only three months after she passed her driver's test at age 77. Dad and I had wondered then whether she would pass the driving test, not because her driving was unsafe but because she might say something to the examiner that would tip him off to what we considered a disability or to her having difficulty in the potentially stressful situation where a stranger was driving with her and grading her ability. Still, it appeared to be an opportunity for an unbiased outsider to set limits. She passed with flying colors. That was May. It was this rapid decline that sharpened our awareness of how fast changes can take place with this disease.

My mother was a good driver for quite some time, and even after being diagnosed with Alzheimer's she drove to the bank, to the cemetery where she walked the dogs, and to the beach for more walks. She drove to get her hair done and to pick up supper items at the grocery store. Those were trips she was so familiar with it was as if she imagined her destination, plugged the coordinates into her mental GPS, and the car drove itself, though often she found herself going to the store when she wanted to go to the hairdresser because they were on the same street.

As time went on, around the second year after symptoms began, my father and I become concerned she would forget to put on the brake and would step on the gas and get into an accident, a la my bakery incident of 1969. Still, each time my father or I drove with her, she seemed completely in control and continued to be an appropriately cautious driver.

When I suggested I drive, she screamed, "This is my car. What gives you the right to drive my car?"

"I'm not looking for any rights. I just thought you might like a break."

"Well, I don't need a break." And off we went. I was not really afraid, but I always glanced in my side mirror and the visor mirror, occasionally saying, "Red light coming," to which she barked, "You don't need to tell me. I can see it!"

Unfortunately, when Mom finally stopped driving, it changed Dad's independence and it changed the dynamics of their relationship. For her to stop driving meant Dad had to be with Mom at all times. When she wanted to go to the store, he had to stop what he was doing and go with her. He also had to convince her to let him go. He couldn't just come out and tell her it wasn't safe for her to drive.

Dad had to hide the car keys in case he might be out in his office off our barn for a short time and Mom might take the car without his knowing. When Mom couldn't find the keys, Dad pretended to look for them then said, "Well, I can't find them. Why don't we go together?"

When I came for a visit and wanted to go to a restaurant or walk the dogs, Mom wanted to drive. I could take my car, but the dogs were afraid to get into it — just what I needed, resistance from other members of the household — and so we'd have to take her car. Of course, she'd want to drive. "I haven't had a chance to drive your car," I'd say. "I hear it's a great car, very smooth. Mind if I drive?" Complimenting her Taurus Wagon — hardly the kind of awe-inspiring car I had built up with my question — usually got me behind the wheel.

She was a back seat driver who made suggestions about where to park, which road to take, how fast to drive. It was especially annoying to have her criticize my speed when I was going under the speed limit on a 35-mph road and had lines of cars behind me. I had to pull over to let them pass.

"Why are you stopping?" she'd ask.

I tried not to let my annoyance show but often responded, "Because you are the only one on this road who thinks I am speeding, so I am letting the parade behind me go ahead."

"I never said you were going fast," she responded.

It was easy to get caught up in Mom's fantasy, thinking I could create a new reality for her. In time I realized my frustration did not warrant verbal involvement. It was just as easy, and far kinder, to tell her I was pulling over because someone was following too closely, and I was worried they'd ram us from behind.

"You're such a safe driver," she'd said with a lovely smile.

About the time my mother became fearful of being left alone, she also became willing to stop driving. There was no great announcement; it just happened. One day Dad noticed she was not asking for her keys or wanting to drive. That was less than six months after her driver's test. I have no idea if it was fear of driving, if she just stopped caring about independence, or if it was something else entirely, but the issue disappeared. She wanted to be with my father or whoever was taking care of her — and by then it did feel more like caretaking than company at times — and it was fine if we were driving. She enjoyed being a passenger, and we enjoyed trips together more. I could point out interesting houses and ask her if she liked them. Her mind seemed clearer. Sometimes she told me a story about who lived here or there or what addition they had put on the house. It was as if her mind, cleared of one focus, opened space for another.

* * *

What works:

- Using excuses that decrease the stress when driving is no longer safe. *Oh, the car is in for a tune-up*, perhaps, or *We can't find the keys to your car, but let's go in mine.*
- Encouraging friends to make invitations that include doing the driving.
- Staying ahead of the curve. Suggest, your keys already

in hand, taking the dog to the field where he loves to run, picking up the packages at the post office, checking out new neighborhoods or going for an ice cream. Instead of an argument, you are on the road again.

4

Driving Her Father's Car

Yielding to Strangers

Of all my friends, I have the best car, a green '66 Mustang with a white convertible top my parents gave me for high school graduation. When the top is down, I put my surfboard in the back so it's sticking out while I drive down the New Hampshire coast, my radio blasting "Wouldn't it be Nice" by the Beach Boys or "Carolina in My Mind" by James Taylor. I especially liked that song because he wrote, "Karin she's a silver sun, you best walk her way and watch her shine..." and he even spelled it my way.

I don't know how to surf, but I look cool driving in my car with my surfboard. I often attract cute, sun-tanned guys who want to give me lessons. "Yeah," I say, "those are surfers' knobs on my knees." Like I even know what that means.

It's my freshman year in college, and I have a pass to keep my car on campus because I lied about having a job that required a car. Mid-year exams start on Monday, but Friday night I'm bored and have studied as much as I want to. I see my friend Sherrie in the dorm. "What are you doing this weekend?" I ask.

"I don't know, probably just getting drunk," she says.

I miss my boyfriend Bill, who is a student at UNC Chapel Hill. "Want to drive down to North Carolina?"

"Sure, but let's pick up Tom. My license is suspended, and he can help with the driving. He just got out of jail and he's not working yet."

This does not sound good, and I weigh whether I should ask Sherrie to drive with a suspended license or let her convict boyfriend drive. "Okay, let's hurry," I say, "because Maine is in the opposite direction."

Route 1 goes all the way from Maine, where we pick up Tom, to North Carolina. We jump on the road in Portsmouth and drive through the night. Sherrie and Tom are making out in the back seat, and I feel like a taxi driver.

Early morning, I decide I better call my mother and tell some story that will keep her from calling me over the weekend. We are near Newark Airport, so we park there, and I find a pay phone in the terminal.

"Mom, I'm studying in the library all weekend, so don't bother to call me, okay?"

Just then, I hear in the background, "United Flight 525 departing from Newark to Los Angeles,"

"I gotta go Mom. I'll call you on Monday."

We keep driving south on Route 1, reach New Brunswick,

New Jersey needing gas. I have no money left in my wallet. I only brought ten dollars with me and I spent it all on gas in Connecticut. Sherrie and the convict have no money either.

We stop at a department store and I ask to see the manager so I can cash a check. A kindly looking man about 40 years old walks toward me, smiling. A good sign.

"What can I do to help you?" he asks.

"I didn't plan very well for a trip to North Carolina, and I would like to cash a check for twenty-five dollars."

"Okay," he says, "may I see your ID?"

"I only have my student ID with me. Will that work?"

"What about your driver's license?"

"I left New Hampshire kind of quickly."

I realize it sounds like I have escaped from jail. I look over at Tom and Sherrie. If the manager is also thinking that, he's not far from the truth. Tom just put a candy bar in his pocket.

"I'll tell you what," he says, "if my daughter were driving to North Carolina without a driver's license, ran out of money and wanted someone to cash a check, I'd want them to, so here's the money," he says, smiling.

I smile back, relieved. Tom pockets a cigarette lighter.

I'm tired and we have a lot of driving ahead of us. I don't really want Tom to drive. I see a guy hitchhiking. I stop and roll down the window. "Where are you going?"

"About an hour down the road. Where are you going?"

"UNC Chapel Hill. Do you have a driver's license?"

"Yeah, why?"

"Want to come?"

"Sure," he says, "I've never been to North Carolina."

Joe Bird is good company on the trip to North Carolina

and drives several hours so I can sleep. I haven't let Bill know I'm coming. It didn't occur to me he might not be there when we arrive. What an idiot I am.

We have been traveling 18 hours when we arrive at Bill's dorm. Thank God he is there and happy to see me. We hang out for a few hours then sleep. I'm up at early. It's time to drive back.

"How'd it take you so long to get here?" Bill asks.

"I drove Route 1 all the way."

Bill roars with laughter. "Oh, my God. Take Route 95. Route 1 goes through every little town. You went through Massachusetts, Rhode Island, Connecticut and down that way?"

"Yup," I say, feeling stupid.

We kiss good-bye, and I promise to call when I get back to New Hampshire. I find Sherrie, Tom and Joe asleep in the dorm common room. Tom is probably stoned. I wonder if I can leave him. He might not notice he's in North Carolina for a few days. Still, since he came with Sherrie, I better take him back. Joe showers and is fresh and ready for the drive.

We drop Joe off at his original destination in DC, and Sherrie, Tom and I drive to New Hampshire. We arrive on campus at midnight. My first exam is at 8:30. I suddenly feel irresponsible and cram for the next six hours and sleep a little.

My escapade earns me a C- in one course, not my usual A or B. More importantly, I learn some life lessons from my spur-of-the-moment travel adventure, some having to do with accepting responsibility for poor decisions. Though she never brought it up, I strongly suspect Mom knew from our conversation I was up to something. Had she interfered, I never would have learned the lesson on my own. Thanks, Mom.

Mom and Dad's cars were held together with ropes, wire and duct tape. They didn't have enough money for new cars, so Dad picked up barely running cars from junk yards and enlisted friends who were handy to make big repairs. Dad was not handy at all but tried on occasion to make his cars work.

Our Studebaker required a rope attached to the clutch pedal to pull the pedal back out. Dad could press the pedal down to disengage the clutch, but the pedal wouldn't come back up on its own. This technique worked until the engine died. Then it was on to the next junker.

This next car burned a quart of oil every 50 miles. When nearing that mark, Dad drove to the local gas station, where the mechanic poured in oil that had been drained from other cars during their oil changes. Black and thick, it didn't matter, since the oil burned so quickly.

During Mom's illness, their way to pass time on many days was to drive the ocean road, look at houses and stop for lunch. One day, as Dad started the car, Mom said, "This is not your car, this is my father's car! How dare you drive his car without permission!"

Dad pulled out the registration and showed it to Mom. "See, it says Ralph White right here. It's my car."

"You are not my Ralph. Stop saying that," Mom replied. "And it's my father's car."

"I am Ralph," he insisted. "See the photo on my license?

Ralph White. See the registration? Ralph White. Doesn't this picture look like me?"

"Yes, but you're not my Ralph."

"Well, I'm the only Ralph you know," he said.

"And you can't drive my father's car!" she yelled, getting out and storming into the house.

Dad called me, sounding frantic. "Karin, your Mom says I'm not Ralph. I've tried to convince her, but it's not working. Maybe you can help." He put Mom on the phone.

"Hi, Mom," I said.

"There's a man here. He says he's my Ralph, but he's not."

"Is he old, with gray hair?"

"Yes."

"That's him, Mom. He just got old. Same guy, different year. I promise you, it's him."

"Okay, if you say so."

I hung up, sure I'd solved the dilemma of the day.

Dad asked Mom again if she wanted to go for a ride.

"Not in my father's car, we're not! And where is my Ralph? I want my Ralph," she said, her voice quavering.

"I'm right here," Dad said.

"Stop saying that! You're not my Ralph. I'm going to go upstairs and look for him."

"You do that," Dad said, frustrated. "I'm going to change my sweater."

Dad walked up the back stairs to his bedroom on the second floor. Mom walked up the front spiral staircase and entered his room just as he finished changing into a red sweater.

"There you are!" she said, "I've been looking everywhere for you!"

Dad realized the changed sweater created a changed Ralph. "Let's go for that ride," he said.

"Not in my father's car. He never said you could drive it."

"Actually," Dad said, "I called him, and he said I could drive it today.

"Okay," Mom said, "since my father said you can drive his car, what are we waiting for? Let's go!"

* * *

What works:

- Going for rides often, stop at overlooks for views, take short walks, talk about which house on the street is your favorite.
- Singing songs together in the car. She might remember the words to songs from her childhood.
- Taking your dogs with you as their presence is a nice distraction. Plus, you can stop to let them run for exercise.
- Avoiding trying to convince your loved one of your identity with facts like driver's licenses, registrations, marriage certificates, and wedding photo albums. You don't look the same and you won't convince her. Be a "good friend" when she is confused. You might be her husband at some time in the future but settle for being a good friend. If she doesn't recognize you, suggest she go look for "you" and try changing your clothes and come back.
- Recognizing if she refers to "her father," she may actually mean you. Roles can become very confused.

5

Mrs. Coffee's Dancing School

Partners for Life

My mother makes me go to Mrs. Coffee's Dancing School in Middlebury, Connecticut to learn ballroom dancing. A seventh grader, all I want to do is slow dance with my arms around a guy's neck and his around my waist. I want to rock back and forth slowly spinning in a tight circle. I do not want to tango or waltz or fox trot across a dance floor. Those dances are for people with gray hair.

My mother says I need to learn how to waltz and fox trot, though probably I can skip the tango.

"That's for old people," I tell her.

"You'll thank me for this one day," she says. "And Sandy, Jane and Patti's parents are making them go too."

Girls have to wear Sunday dresses, white ankle socks and

black patent leather shoes. We also have to wear white gloves like Jackie Kennedy and Audrey Hepburn. In my book, they are old people too.

"I don't dress up this much on Easter Sunday," I say, staring in the mirror at the cranberry dress with white lace collar that my grandmother bought in Filene's Department store. "I look stupid. And I'm not wearing those gloves. I don't know where they are anyway."

"If you would just leave them in one spot, you'd always find them," comes Mom's muffled voice from upstairs.

I'd like to leave them in the trash.

"Here are your grandmother's elbow length gloves," she says. "You can roll them down."

"I'd rather wear Dad's work gloves," I say.

It is almost time to go. "Here they are," I say with little enthusiasm, having known all the time they were in the back of my underwear drawer.

"From now on, just leave them in the..." Mom starts laughing. She always laughs at her jokes before she says the punch line. "Just leave them in the car glove compartment."

Those of us whose parents think ballroom dancing a skill we need to master like potty training or driving cram into a car every Wednesday for the twenty-minute ride from Woodbury to Middlebury. Rolf, Robin, Paul, Jane, Patti, Sandy and I are squished into Ford station wagons made for four passengers and a driver. We are so tight we have to alternate placement of our arms – one forward and one pressed back to the seat – in order to fit.

Rolf is sitting next to me. I can't move the entire trip, or my left breast will rub against his right arm. I angle my body away from Paul so I can't smell his body odor and instead engage in unintentional contact with Rolf. I hear Rolf's quick shallow breathing through his mouth. I run through times tables in my head. Finally, we tumble out of the car.

"Have a great time," Sandy's Mom says. "I'll be back in an hour."

The boys run ahead of us to get inside the town hall to see their friends. Dance class is adjacent to the town offices in a large gymnasium with wooden floors and folding metal chairs along each side of the room. The room is multi-purpose with a stage at one end. Basketball bleachers are folded closed and pressed to the side walls under cranked up basketball backboards.

The boys huddle together in a corner under the score board with their hands in their pockets, occasionally glancing over at the girls, who are divided in small groups. There are the cool girls, the slightly less cool – my group with Sandy, Jane and Patti – and the rejects. The girls who go to private schools are in the cool group regardless of how they look or act. They stand up straighter, have confident smiles, and wear Lilly Pulitzer dresses. Sandy, Jane, Patti and I wear dresses with uneven hems we made in Home Economics class. The rejects wear their mother's dresses.

The boys wear white shirts and pull their clip-on ties out of their pants pockets moments before class starts. These classes are as much a joke to them as they are to us. But there is a difference in roles between the boys and girls at Mrs. Coffee's Dancing School. The boys get to ask the girls to dance.

Mrs. Coffee enters from the stage and walks down wooden steps to the gymnasium floor. She wears a white dress cinched tight at the waist with a patent leather belt. The bodice is fitted, and translucent sleeves cover her arms. Her hair is styled in a French twist, her hair brushed back off her face. It looks plastered with hair spray because it never moves and no pieces stray from their position, even during a raucous jitterbug. Mrs. Coffee claps castanets to get our attention. We stop talking and turn in her direction.

"Tonight, ladies and gentlemen, we are going to learn the waltz," she says as if we are dancing for the Queen of England.

As soon as she announces a dance, the boys start fidgeting because they know one of them is going to be chosen as Mrs. Coffee's partner. She likes to dance with Grant. We all do. He is the most handsome boy in class with long eyelashes and dark hair. His smile reveals brilliant white teeth that are straight without braces. He looks right into your eyes when he dances with you. He has only chosen me once, and I forgot to swallow my saliva and drooled. Grant is in the cool group but occasionally he chooses someone from the second tier to dance with.

"Grant, come demonstrate how to do the waltz," Mrs. Coffee says, smiling demurely. All the boys other than Grant breathe a collective sigh of relief. Grant puts his arm around Mrs. Coffee's waist and holds her white-gloved hand as she leads him in the waltz. "One, two three. One, two, three," Mrs. Coffee says. "See how easy it is? Now, choose partners."

This is the part of class I hate the most about dancing school. All the boys line up on one side of the gym and the girls on the others. We sit with our fingers laced together and hands in our laps. Our ankles have to be crossed and off to one side. The boys head straight for Jane. She has blond hair in a perfect page boy, wears a short, flowered dress and ankle socks with lace trim. I have mismatched gloves, a pudgy baby face, and a dress I found on the floor of my closet five minutes before the carpool arrived. Sandy is too tall for the boys except Gusty, so she slouches to try and look shorter. Gusty wants to dance with Jane, too, but at six feet tall, he has to settle for Sandy, who is also six feet tall. Sometimes he chooses me, and I have to reach my arms straight to the sky to dance with him. Patti is pretty and has been wearing a bra for a year, so the boys like her too. But Jane is their number one choice.

Paul likes to dance with me and pulls me close to him, our chests touching. I have to use all my strength to keep the one, two, three waltz going while pulling the lower half of my body away from him. This causes us to move closer together with our top halves. Which means his body odor rubs off on my dress.

Finally, the hour is over. Mrs. Coffee waves good-bye. "See you next week! Remember, practice at home!"

Sandy's mother drops me off. I run inside, go straight upstairs, throw my dress on the closet floor, and shove my gloves back in my underwear drawer. Sure, Mrs. Coffee. I'll invite my friends over to practice waltzing. Just like my Mom and Dad. Old folks dancing around the living room.

When my mother was well, my parents loved to dance. Mom placed her right hand on my father's back with the palm facing out, as if her hand had been amputated and sewn on backwards. My mother must have seen that hand positioning somewhere and adopted it as her own. Or, like holding a teacup with the pinky extended upward, she thought it looked refined.

When they danced the jitterbug, though, she placed her hand on Dad's back, fingers down, then pulled away and held Dad's hand, leaving her left hand free. Together, then apart, then right hand still holding Dad's left, he swung her hand over her head and spun her in a circle. Sometimes Mom reached behind to meet Dad's hand as he spun her part way and then, as if she were on a hinge, pushed her back the other way.

They had an original technique in which they opened their stances and stood side-by-side, one arm around each waist. Then in beat with a hesitation step — almost a step-touch — they walked several steps forward. They added funny facial and body expressions. Dad's mouth made a tight "O" and he rocked his shoulders left and right; Mom smiled a toothy grin and put an exaggerated bounce in her step. After the walking move, they came back together in a standard jitterbug.

When they danced at clubs or ballrooms, people stopped eating or talking to friends when Mom and Dad danced. Sometimes there was a circle of enthusiastic clappers while they danced in the center. At the end of each dance, Mom and Dad received rounds of applause.

After five years at home, Dad felt it was better to have Mom live in a residential community that could better serve her increasing difficulties. He chose a facility called Sprucewood. When Dad arrived every day to visit Mom, he almost immediately worked to get her moving. Given the routine of her life and the limitations of her disease, it was difficult to come up with activities they could do together. But dancing was one they enjoyed. If she was asleep when he arrived, he awakened her then gently pulled her out of her chair into a standing position. She opened her eyes and smiled when she saw him.

"How about we dance a little?" Dad asked. There was no music, so he sang "Bill Bailey" or "She'll be Coming Round the Mountain" or "Chattanooga Choo Choo." Their movements were smaller than when they used to dance, and the circles were tighter. Mom still moved in time to the beat of the song although her steps were no more than a lift of the heel and a shift of a couple of inches. She smiled as she danced and focused on my father's face.

If the staff was doing karaoke, Mom and Dad danced. When Mom first entered a care facility and she was in better physical condition, she and Dad danced and moved around the floor in front of other residents who sat in chairs and watched. When they finished, the residents clapped.

"The entertainment was very good today," Dad overheard one resident say.

"Did you hear that Shirl? They think we're professionals!" Dad joked.

When walking the halls, Dad tried to keep Mom stepping in time to a song, his arm around her waist, both to keep her steady and to simulate the unique dance movement they used to do. Pushing Mom to walk a little faster was good for her because with Alzheimer's Disease some people develop Parkinson-like symptoms and shuffle. The dancing and faster walking stimulated muscle memory and encouraged her body to go to old movements rather than settle for the shuffling that took less effort.

Even when Mom didn't want to leave her chair, Dad could get her moving if he sang or if music was playing. Often when I visited, I tuned into the website Pandora.com. I created the station "Big Band" or "Frank Sinatra" and music played from the website. Dad also kept a set of CDs handy with a light-weight portable CD player. Music was easily accessible, allowing Mom and Dad to dance often.

Not only did Mom get exercise and enjoy the movement, Mom and Dad experienced something that gave them pleasure. Dad didn't care that they were not swinging in a wild jitterbug. He was happy they had an activity they could experience together.

I enjoyed dancing with Mom when I visited. Sometimes I acted goofy to make her laugh. Sometimes I was serious and held her in a ballroom dance position.

"Come on Mom," I said, "let's try a waltz for good old Mrs. Coffee. One, two, three. One, two, three!"

* * *

What works:

- Playing music. Pandora.com is a music genome that takes the songs and artists you love and creates a unique station. It's especially helpful at holiday times.
- Making sure your loved one is steady on her feet before dancing. Once steady, the positioning for dancing allows support.
- Dancing, as long as she wants. If she is keeping a beat, she is dancing.

- "Dancing" in a chair if your loved one cannot dance standing. If you can't get feet moving, get arms moving.
- Stepping in time to music while walking down the hall. "We're off to see the wizard" was a favorite to get Mom moving.
- Putting songs from their era on your phone or other device and connect it to a portable speaker for instant music. Or telling Siri on Apple or Alexa on Amazon to play a favorite artist.

6

Adeste Fideles

Singing Your Heart Out

I have a concert-sized 12-string guitar that is so large I can barely hold it. It is the same size guitar Judy Collins plays. I can play "Both Sides Now," "Where Have all the Flowers Gone?" and a bunch of other folk songs that can be played with only three chords — G, C, D — and a couple of variations of those chords. There are other chords in folk songs, like F, but I am too lazy to learn F. There are too many fingers involved. I'm looking for easy chords. Traditional folk songs are pretty simple, but if a note doesn't work with my trio of chords, I just skip over it until I can pick the song up at G, C or D.

Sandy, Patti, Jane and I enter a talent contest. We practice "500 Miles" and "Lemon Tree" and perfect our harmonies. Sandy and I play guitars.

But, before the big day comes, we have to have outfits.

Matching outfits. Jane and I know how to sew, Patti is too cool to sew and Sandy failed Home Economics. We convince our parents to let us take the bus into Waterbury, Connecticut, the biggest city I have ever visited, to shop at Worth's Department Store. We have a budget and a goal, to find something all four of us like and that likes all four of us.

One problem. We are all different in height, weight and development. At 13, Sandy is six feet tall. Jane is petite, slim, and as we tell her "flat as a board." Patti and I have already developed. Anything that fits Jane will not fit the three of us. Any skirt that fits Sandy is to our ankles. We decide on white oxford cloth blouses and herringbone black and white skirts hemmed to hit us mid-thigh.

On the day of the talent show, when we step on stage, the gymnasium looks like a college stadium. In spite of our nervousness, our harmonies are perfect. The outfits are a bit frumpy but match. We win second place. When I get home, Mom and Dad have me play the songs again. "You should have won first place," Dad says.

At Mom's memory unit, music was an important activity because many people with Alzheimer's can sing familiar songs from their pasts. Patriotic songs they grew up on are especially easy, "America the Beautiful," for instance. Other familiar songs for Mom's generation and older are "Don't Sit Under the Apple Tree," "She'll Be Coming 'Round the Mountain" or "I've Been Working on the Railroad."

The unit had song books and many residents could still read the lyrics. Some enjoyed singing solos and had no inhibitions, singing loudly and clearly, often perfectly on pitch.

They knew all the words. Others were unable to participate but seemed content to watch and listen.

We kept thinking Mom would enjoy singing, but she never joined in. Dad knew how much she enjoyed singing when she was well and encouraged her, but the best she could ever could do was mouth the words.

Dad realized the residents loved to sing, especially when there was instrumental accompaniment, but discovered the musicians could come only once a week. Dad decided to learn how to play the guitar. He was 80 years old.

"Do you think I can learn?" he asked me. "I hear a lot of songs are played with only three chords."

"That's true. I only really know G, C and D, and I can play lots of the old tunes."

"The other problem," he said, "is that I can't sing. I try in church, but I'm tone deaf. I love to sing, but I'm terrible."

"It doesn't matter, Dad, and you're not terrible. Play and do the best you can. That's what counts." I often sat next to him in church and remember especially his "*Adeste Fideles*" sung at loud volume, each note missing the pitch a bit. It never bothered me because I knew how much he loved to sing. If I sang louder than he did, I could often pull him onto the right note.

Dad found a music school, bought a guitar, a stand, a metronome and a special tuning device.

"I told the teacher what I was doing," Dad said, "and that I wanted songs that only have three chords, But Todd didn't understand I only want to learn three chords and to play songs with those three chords. He's got songs with three chords, but each song has three different chords. I don't think I can learn to play this guitar."

I took lyrics from his favorite songs, pulled out my old guitar, and started with G. When I heard a chord change coming, I changed to C or D. It was usually one of those chords. If songs didn't use those three chords, I dropped them from the list. "O Susannah" — G, C and D. "She'll be Coming 'Round the Mountain," — same three. Dad's list grew.

One day Todd said he wasn't going to charge Dad for lessons anymore.

"I have plenty of money," Dad said. "So, if you're worried I can't pay, I can."

"No," Todd said. "When I found out you were learning to play guitar so you could play for your wife, I decided I couldn't charge you anymore. If I charge you, I won't feel I'm a part of what you are doing. This is what music is about, sharing it with people. I want to contribute to what you are doing. I'm not going to charge you anymore."

Each week, Dad played a special concert, including folk songs and patriotic standards using only G, C and D chords. He even could play "Adeste Fideles."

"Do I make a fool of myself when I sing?" Dad asked me. "I know I don't sing on tune, but am I close?"

"You are perfect, Dad."

* * *

What Works

- Singing songs that have easy tunes. Add old hymns to the repertoire.
- Including accompaniment. Maracas, bongos, even toilet paper tubes covered at both ends with dry beans inside make great percussion.
- Playing the guitar even if you can't play perfectly. No one notices if you play the wrong chord. If you hit a spot in the song and don't have the right chord, keeping singing and start playing again when the song meets the chord you know.
- Clapping when you sing if someone else is playing. It adds to the enjoyment and it's good practice at keeping rhythm.
- Celebrating any holiday: Mother's Day, St. Patrick's Day, Flag Day. You can always find songs that go with a theme. When in doubt, Google.

7

Baby Magic

Lots of Cuddles

Mom stops in front of a shopping cart carrying a child of about four. Clearly, the child does not want to be in the child seat and feels she is too big for the carriage. But in the eyes of her mother, the child is too curious and demanding to walk the aisles. So, she sits in the carriage and screams. Loud, long screams with her head held back and all her teeth showing, tears streaming down her face, her shirt already wet from the aisle before.

"What, what is that I hear?" Mom says cocking her head to one side. "I think I hear, yes, I hear, could it be, Santa Claus calling me?"

The child slows and quiets but keeps whimpering. "What is that Santa?" Mom continues. "What did you say? There is a sweet girl in the cereal aisle?"

By now, the mother is intrigued, if not relieved. Any moment of silence is enjoyed by the mother and certainly by the rest of the shoppers.

"Oh, yes, she has been such a good girl," Mom says. "Yes, oh yes, she deserves lots of presents!" Mom has the attention of both mother and child now; the little girl wipes away a tear. "Yes, oh yes, Santa Claus, she is going to continue to be good in the store."

Mom puts her finger to her mouth and gives a conspiratory "shhhhh" to the little girl.

"Yes, she won't ask for anything she isn't supposed to have. Yes, yes, Santa, I'll tell her."

Turning to the little girl, Mom says, "Santa told me you should go to bed early on Christmas Eve and sleep very late in the morning. When you go downstairs, he will have left you lots of presents." The little girl smiles. The mother mouths the words "thank you" and we all continue shopping.

My mother stopped strangers with babies in stores, on streets, at the park. She liked to make faces, poke, tickle and entertain. She was especially clever on airplanes, distracting children by playing games and thus relieving stressed parents. She created toys out of found objects: the emergency booklet in the back of the seat pocket on the airplane became a hide and seek shield, keys in her purse could be jingled and chewed, and in the days when smoking was allowed on planes, she slipped the cellophane wrapper off her package of Kent cigarettes and rustled it to make a distracting noise. It never occurred to her to ask permission to poke a baby's belly or hide behind a seat and pop her head out and say, "Boo!" When in the presence of children, Mom was on stage.

She was especially good in grocery stores, those halls of

temptation for young children with hands grabbing colorful foods, forbidden items, and worst, breakable products. Mom could spot a melee from aisles away – crying children, screams about the brand of cereal, mothers repeating over and over, "Keep your hands in the cart. No, we are not getting Trix, or Coco Puffs! Stop asking me!" While other shoppers fled or scowled, Mom sought out the child and distracted him or her.

I must admit, the child development people will wince when I confess I "talked" to Santa and the Easter Bunny many times over the years when my children were cranky in the car or having a temper tantrum in public. I am further ashamed to admit my telepathic conversations with Santa began in September and ended on December 25. The Easter Bunny and I communicated from February to Easter. I'm quite sure Mom used the same tricks on my brother and me.

In Alzheimer's residences, people often bring dogs as therapy. Mom enjoyed visits from dogs, but we were surprised she was only lukewarm about their presence since she had lived her entire life with a dog or three until she moved to Sprucewood.

But bring a baby to see Mom and her entire countenance changed. Immediately, her eyes lifted. Her whole head, downward cast from so much sleep all day, lifted and her neck straightened.

When I brought our granddaughter Karina to visit after Mom had Alzheimer's for about seven years, she appeared to recognize our son, Tim, and his wife, Marie, as a part of her world. She easily held Karina when she posed for pictures and was relatively aware of her surroundings and our family gathering.

Two and a half years later, our daughter Christie gave birth to a girl. By then, Mom was in a different facility as her health had declined and she needed more attention. She was in the habit of sitting for long periods, observing activities but not participating. We met her in the activity room to introduce her to her new great-granddaughter, Lilly.

"Hi Mom," I said getting down to her eye level. "Look who we have here!"

"This is your great-granddaughter," Christie said.

Mom immediately focused on Lilly and smiled. Her face lit up. We doubt she recognized the relationship of this child to its mother or to her own daughter, but she recognized this little squirmy being as a baby. She reached out and clearly said, "Pretty baby." Mom rarely spoke and when she did, her words were generally garbled and impossible to understand. But she clearly said, "pretty baby." She stroked Lilly's hand.

We were nervous about letting Mom hold such a small baby, but we negotiated her positioning. Christie sat on one side and I on the other. We put Lilly in Mom's lap, and Christie and I stretched an arm from each side. Mom held onto Lilly as if it were the most comfortable position she knew, muscle memory of holding babies taking over. She carefully put her arms around Lilly's waist and held her loosely but firmly, Christie and I serving as seat belts.

Mom looked down at Lilly's head and smiled, then she smiled at me. It made me happy to see her happy. We took a photo of the four generations as we had with Mom, Karina, Tim and wife a few years earlier. I was struck by the difference in her physical condition. Before, Mom had been able to walk fairly easily from room to room. She held Karina without assistance and made finger movements like she had on a finger puppet. She knew she was entertaining Karina. This time, she was enjoying the simple warmth of Lilly in her arms and the pleasure of seeing a baby. I believe she knew the concept that this was a baby and remembered she loved babies. Clearly, she did not comprehend her relationship to Lilly. Even clearer to me was the knowledge that it didn't matter.

Mom didn't know my name or her grandchildren's names or her great-grandchildren's names. People think that someone with Alzheimer's needs to know your name, know your relationship to them. (I try not to get irritated by the question I am always asked, "Does she know you?") That is not the point. People with Alzheimer's enjoy the moment, live in the moment. That is all they have. The opportunity to bring special moments to people with Alzheimer's is key to making their lives better.

When we brought Karina to see Mom years before, it was to introduce her to her first great grandchild. When we brought Lilly to see Mom, it was to give her an opportunity to respond on a level of a special kind of memory, the one that drew her to little children, to try and relate to them on their level.

At her last Christmas, Mom was surrounded by five grandchildren. Tim and Marie had twins following Karina's birth, and Christie had one more daughter after Lilly. The children crawled up her legs and over her body. Mom giggled, posed for pictures and offered pieces of cookie. They took turns sitting on Mom's walker and were wheeled through the halls. We sang Christmas carols while the little ones danced or clapped their hands. It was clear to me that Mom and babies had always been on a special wavelength, perhaps even more so with her Alzheimer's.

* * *

What works:

- Bringing babies as often as possible. Friends will ask what they can do. Tell them to bring their children or grandchildren. The children accept the person with Alzheimer's exactly how she is.
- Bringing photo albums of family members when they were babies. Talk about each person in the photos.
- Making books at shutterfly.com or any new technology that works for you. Looking through the albums and telling stories.
- Having coloring books and toys available for children who visit. And you never know when your loved one might feel like coloring.
- Finding photos of babies in magazines and paste them into scrap books.
- Letting your loved one hold a baby with your help.

8

Jewelry Boxes

Hunting for Treasure

Our Mom has a box of costume jewelry, always a huge tangle of necklaces and earrings, stored in a miniature Lane cedar chest, its top secured by only one hinge so it lists to one side when I open it. There are treasures — like a pirate's booty — strings of pearls with silver and rhinestone clasps, necklaces with chunks of fake jade interspersed with gold beads and dangling black earrings with sequin edges.

My brother Eric and I love to dress up in Mom's costume jewelry, loading on multiple necklaces, screwing earrings on and off, and strutting around the bedroom like we are getting ready for Cinderella's ball.

The attachment of earrings to ear lobes is painful business. First, we have to unscrew the backing, opening a space in the earring to slip it over the ear lobe. Then we screw in a small metal disc until it comes in tight contact with the back of the lobe, like a little ear vise.

"I don't want to wear lipstick," Eric says, but I make him let me paint it on. I show him how to smack his lips together, like Mom does, then blot the lipstick on a folded tissue. I put a little on my cheeks like Mom, and rub it in. We look in the mirror and giggle. A blue bottle of Evening in Paris sits on her mirrored bureau top, and a little dab behind the ears and on the wrists completes our imitation. We slip our feet into wobbly spike heels, grab cigarettes from her Kent packet, and parade around bedroom pretending to smoke.

"You always get the diamond necklace," Eric says.

"I'm older. I get to pick first," I say.

"Not fair!"

None of Mom's jewelry is valuable, and anything she especially cares about is put in a separate jewelry box. So, it doesn't matter if or how we return the tangled mess of pearls, chains and earrings to the rickety box.

One day, I walk into Mom's bedroom to play with her jewelry and find her crying.

"What's the matter?" I whisper. The only other time I remember seeing my mother cry was when our cocker spaniel Amos died.

"I lost the diamond in my engagement ring," she says. "I don't know when I lost it, but it's gone."

My mother's engagement ring is a modest diamond surrounded by a ring of gold in a large, simple setting so the stone looks larger than it is. She is holding the ring with empty gold prongs, like the hole in a tooth where a filling fell out.

I start searching on her bureau, crawl on the floor and run my hand over the brown and white shag carpet. But, if the diamond has fallen on the rug, I'll never find it. The pile is too thick and the room too big. Anyway, we both know it could have fallen out anywhere. "Will Dad be mad?"

"No, of course not," she says. "He'll see how sad I am," and she continues to cry.

In the early 70's, a friend of my mother named Art challenged her to give up smoking. She smoked five cigarettes a day, a few more if she went to a party. And when five were smoked in a day, she smoked no more. I smoked in high school to be cool, though instead of becoming one of the top tier of cool kids, I became hooked on nicotine. When Mom's friend suggested they try to stop smoking, Mom thought it would set a good example and help me to quit.

They agreed to quit. If Mom started smoking again, she had to give Art $500, which meant going to my father for $500. She didn't have that kind of money herself. If Art smoked first, he would buy Mom an emerald ring. I had no idea my mother even liked emeralds, let alone wanted one, but that was the deal.

I could have predicted the outcome. Anyone who could control her smoking to five cigarettes a day, who would have to ask my father for $500 to pay off a bet, who was as competitive as my mother, would never lose. Art made it a few months. Mom got an emerald ring set in a simple gold setting. She wore it for special occasions, but it never looked natural on her finger. With only a gold wedding band on her left hand and the emerald on her right, it looked like her hands were competing for attention, leaving the gold band looking dull and forlorn against the flashy green sparkler.

On their 20th wedding anniversary, Mom and Dad took us to Bermuda for a week. It was the first time Eric and I had been on a plane. At age 14, I thought it had to be the most exotic, exciting, and beautiful place on earth. We played on the pink sand beaches, rode on the backs of my parents' motor bikes, and swam in the clear waters.

Dad bought Mom another diamond ring.

"I didn't have money when we got engaged, but I do now," he said, "so I want her to have a nice ring." This time the diamond sat elegantly among gold prongs, high above the ring itself. She slipped it on her left hand on top of her gold band and never again wore a ring on her other hand.

In the early stages of Mom's Alzheimer's, she developed the habit of twirling her diamond ring around her finger and taking it off and putting it back on, taking it off and putting it on a shelf, the table, her bureau, or in her pocket. She once spent hours searching for the ring, and we found it in a pewter cup on a top shelf along with a bracelet misplaced the week before. One time it was sitting on the dirt in the pot of a houseplant like a seed sprouting first leaves.

We suggested she never take the ring off, but the disease does not listen to reason, nor does it remember suggestions. So, each day we watched her take-it-off-put-it-on routine, resigned that the diamond ring would someday be lost. Dad took insurance out on it, knowing he would eventually put in a claim.

One day when I was shopping in Walmart, I saw a ring in

the jewelry department for $40 that looked a lot like Mom's diamond ring. I thought we could exchange it with the real ring and, since they looked so much alike, Mom wouldn't know the difference. We felt a bit dishonest making the switch, but Dad wrapped it up as a gift, and when she took off the real one to try on the other, Dad put the real one in his pocket. I put the anniversary ring in the safe deposit box along with the emerald ring Art gave her.

Eventually, the $40 ring disappeared. In its place grew a wild assortment of costume jewelry. The residents "shopped" in each other's rooms and retrieved the oddest arrays of items. The shiniest jewelry got exchanged the most. Some days Mom had a tennis bracelet of "diamonds and sapphires." This turned up on Clare's wrist too. Eileen shopped more for shoes. She walked the halls non-stop, except to visit friends and dig through their closets for shoes. One day she walked the hall with a tennis shoe on one foot and a loafer on the other. Another day she had on just one tennis shoe. I found the other in my mother's closet. It was Eileen's shoe but in Mom's closet. "Should I help her put it on?" I asked one of the aides. "No, just leave it outside the door. She'll find it."

The funniest item Mom wore was a plastic "decoder" ring, the type kids get in cereal boxes. I suspected a child visiting a grandparent brought it. It was a big, black plastic ring with a silver horse head on it. Mom loved it for a week then Clare wore it.

We learned to leave the good jewelry home. As much as my father wanted to duplicate Mom's life and the way she always looked, put together, well-dressed, everything matching, he gave up on real jewelry. She seemed to find what she wanted on her daily shopping trips at the Alzheimer's Unit "store."

* * *

What works:

- Substituting inexpensive jewelry for the real thing. It might feel dishonest, but it's better to lose fake items.
- Looking at today with the perspective of how the individual lived and dressed prior to having Alzheimer's. My mother always looked put together with nice clothes, well-coifed hair, and lipstick. Make that a priority whether living at home or in a facility. It keeps an aspect of the personality intact.
- Keeping your loved one in nice clothes but ones that are easy to get in and out of, like matching sweat suits.
- Letting your loved one wear costume jewelry. If it makes her happy, it doesn't matter how wild she may look or if it is appropriate.
- Bringing the box of costume jewelry and leave it out on the bureau. Others will "borrow" from it, but that means they are enjoying the jewelry also.

9

HMS Pinafore

Carpe Diem

Mrs. Roberts is my eighth-grade teacher, loves theatre and directs a musical or operetta every year. Short and stocky, her bosom hangs over her waistband as she bangs out songs on the piano. Her hair is pulled back in a severe bun, stray hairs sticking out from the frame of her face but tamed with an occasional lick of the hand and press to the head.

Mrs. Roberts's glasses slide down her nose, making it easy for her to surreptitiously glance from piano to chorus and yell at any student passing notes. She can play a song and in beat holler, "Billy Jones, why don't you come up to the front of the class and read the note you have wadded up so carefully and thrown across the room at Miss Picket." Mrs. Roberts is multi-talented.

Mrs. Roberts chooses "HMS Pinafore" for our performance. I don't know how she is able to control 60 eighth graders for rehearsals, costume fittings, set production and the performance itself. Perhaps it is because we are afraid of her wrath should we step out of line.

Mrs. Roberts's form of character direction is to demonstrate each part, whether male or female. She can sing all the parts in her fake soprano voice, in a baritone or tenor, flitting across the stage or swaggering like a man. She thinks she has a great singing voice, but we have to stifle giggles when she sings.

We make our entrances on time, never moving from our marks. We do not snicker when Terry sings, "I am the captain of the Pinafore" and the sailors answer, "And a right good captain, too!"

There are not enough boys for sailors and Mrs. Roberts says that four girls will have to take those parts. I do not want to be a sailor. A sailor is a boy. I am a girl and want a girl part. I try out for Buttercup in front of the entire class. My voice is lovely – I see in Mrs. Roberts's eyes that I have an edge over Linda. It is down to the two of us and we have one more test. Crying. Buttercup cries in HMS Pinafore.

Linda's turn first. She cries daintily, dabbing her eyes with a handkerchief. (Mrs. Roberts had not mentioned we could use props.) Linda has bright red hair and her eyes always are bloodshot and droopy like she has been crying all day and night. (Not fair.)

"That is so fake," Sandy whispers, daring to bring on the wrath of Mrs. Roberts, who really does seem to have eyes in the back of her head. "She is not going to get it. Her crying is stupid!"

My turn. Remember a sad time, I tell myself. I see my beagle Wags hit by a car. That was very sad, but in front of the entire eighth grade, I can't cry for real. So, I pretend I am an actress in a movie and cry then cry some more. Deep sobs followed by air-sucking even greater sobs. Body shaking, I seem wracked with grief. I can practically see myself taking a curtain call as Buttercup.

"That will be enough, Karin," Mrs. Roberts says, a new look in her eyes. Is it disgust? Disappointment? She licks her hand and pushes her hair back. "We are looking for sadness, not tragedy. This is not Scarlet O'Hara. This is Buttercup." I have no clue who Scarlet O'Hara is. Linda smiles, rheumy eyes laughing at my performance.

I am cast as a sailor. So are Sandy, Patti and Jane. At least we can suffer together.

It is time for one of our many dress rehearsals, a week before the show. The entire cast is on stage and Mrs. Roberts is yelling at the sailors who are not swaying in time. The four of us, the only girls dressed as boy sailors, are intentionally swaying the wrong way, acting as if it is a mistake. Half the real boy sailors sway left (the way they are supposed to) and we sway right. Just as we are being chastised once more, a sailor runs off stage left and then we hear a splash like someone has thrown a bucket of water on the floor.

All eyes turn stage left. "Boys and girls, we are in rehearsal. Pay attention!" yells Mrs. Roberts with two hand claps. She obviously has not caught the premature exit of one of her male sailors.

Then the odor of vomit fills the air and those of us near stage left start retching. "Gross!" yells someone. We all hurry off stage right. Rehearsal over.

It is Ricky. Rumors fly as to what happened. "He had the flu... he ate something bad... he was so afraid of Mrs. Roberts he threw up..." I whisper in Sandy's ear, "I hope it wasn't when the captain sang, 'I'm hardly ever sick at sea!'"

"He has epilepsy, you know," she says.

Epilepsy. I ask my mother what that is, and she tells me it means a sickness where a person has fainting spells and shakes all over. You have to stick a ruler in the person's mouth to keep him from swallowing his tongue or biting it off. It takes a while for the scary shaking to stop, she says, but then the person is okay, even though he doesn't remember much of what happened. There is medicine to fix it. Did Ricky have an epileptic spell and then threw up? I didn't see him shaking.

During rehearsals, we keep our distance from Ricky. I don't know if it is the fear of getting thrown up on or the epilepsy. We are afraid we might catch it. Or that people might associate us with that epileptic kid if we are friends with him. Through high school, every time I see him, I picture him falling down, shaking on the floor. As an adult, I feel sad that we branded him as different because of his epilepsy, because of the idea, even, he might have a seizure.

When Mom had her seizure, Dad was called to the hospital by the staff. After Mom was resting comfortably, Dad called to give me the news.

"The doctors think we should consider starting Mom on anti-seizure medicine," he told me. "On the other hand, they think this could have been an isolated incident. They are not sure they want to throw off the balance of medications she is taking now. It might never happen again."

Mom entered a nursing facility for a week to recover from the seizures and gain strength. Her regular residence was not equipped to handle the special diet of thickened food and drink required to avoid choking. She improved enough to return to the facility and was greeted as a long-lost family member. However, a nurse told me Mom seemed unresponsive for days. "We thought we lost her," Susan said. "Her personality seemed to have disappeared."

Dad slept in her room because she was unsteady on her feet and the staff was unable to provide one-on-one care to make sure she didn't fall. After about three days, she started smiling again, her gait was normal, and she was able to walk with little assistance.

Nine months later, she had another seizure and another trip to the hospital. This time the doctors wanted to be sure of the diagnosis. Was it a seizure or a stroke? There was a small window of time for the appropriate medical response to a stroke. While time passed and the doctors continued to discuss her symptoms, Mom had another episode in the emergency room. This time the doctors were sure it was a seizure. Dad said it was hard to witness but he was glad the diagnosis was definitive.

Again, she went to a nursing facility, but this time it was a longer stay as she recovered more slowly. I visited there to give my evaluation of her condition. She was in a hospital bed, her hair combed back like Elvis Presley. Not flattering, not her style. I combed it into bangs. She smiled when I spoke to her or made goofy faces to illicit a response. I got her to take a walk down the hall with me. She was steady on her feet, although she didn't like walking over thresholds.

An Alzheimer's consultant told us this was common, that the staff sometimes put black tape in areas they didn't want patients to cross because they won't step over the line.

Days later, she had a vacant expression and was not responsive to Dad. She could not follow simple instructions such as being asked to turn and sit. Dad was discouraged by her lack of progress and afraid she wouldn't be able to return to Sprucewood. "This nursing home is depressing," he told me. I agreed. The people there were ill. No, they were dying. It seemed as if a person passed through the doors alive and left dead. We had to get her out.

Dad has a way of convincing anyone his point of view is the correct one. He is skilled in evaluation, reasoning, and problem solving. In discussing Mom's situation, he presented good arguments for her returning to Sprucewood. After all, we saw many residents there confined to wheelchairs, spoon fed meals, and unresponsive.

"I don't want to win this debate and find out I'm wrong," Dad said. "Just because I can find compelling arguments for Mom to return doesn't mean I'm right. Since I want her to get out of this nursing home quickly, I might win the argument and find I've talked her way into an unsafe situation."

Instead, he let the experts decide. The staff at Sprucewood said they were not equipped to handle Mom's needs. If Mom stayed in her chair or used a walker, they could handle her, but Mom was more likely to get up without warning and try to walk. None of us could risk another seizure and fall.

With the help of his consultant, Dad found a new facility that had just opened. The patient-staff ratio was lower, and they could accommodate her special needs. Since they were newly opened, there were many available rooms. Dad chose one that faced a field of wildflowers.

"I know it sounds corny," the director said, "but I wake up every day and think how lucky I am to get to go to work at this job." This statement convinced me this was the right move.

With the help of a neurologist, Mom's medication was re-balanced. Her first anti-seizure medication was probably the same kind that Ricky used in the 60's. The doctor said there were better drugs available. Weaning her from one and intro-ducing her to another with some overlap, we saw her come back to life. Her smiles were real rather than frozen. She re-sponded to people's presence. She slept less.

As the disease slowed her down, it also felt as if it was speeding her toward death. Alzheimer's disease was taking her away from us, substituting her with someone different — someone thinner, less responsive, frailer. I became more pre-pared for the next phase of the disease. Or her next fall. When my father called, I evaluated his tone of voice in split seconds. I used to be immediately fearful when he spoke, but I had learned that tired can sound like scared or the prelude to re-porting a bad incident. I stayed in the moment and waited to react until I had all the information. Staying in the moment was key to living with this disease – staying in her moment and staying in my moment.

* * *

What works:

- Talking to all medical people involved — The primary physician who knows her best, the staff at her residence and the specialists.
- Asking questions about medication benefits, side effects and dosages.
- Keeping good records on file to refer to when speaking with a professional.
- Calling the doctor and asking to leave a message on your phone that it's okay to take a certain medicine. Often your loved one will refuse to take her medication and showing the prescription bottle does not always work. She wants to hear the direction from her doctor. Keep the message and play it every time there is a conflict with taking medicine.
- Remembering when the medication makes a patient into a "zombie" it is not necessarily permanent.
- Thinking "quality of life." How can we improve it?
- Hearing the music, even on dark days.

10

A New Pair of Glasses

Clear Sight

Jane tells me Bob Bennett likes girls in glasses. Bob chases her on the playground and whispers in her ear, "I like your blue glasses."

Jane thinks it is ridiculous that Bob likes her because of her glasses. I think, I want glasses so Bob will chase me on the playground. But I can see perfectly and don't need glasses. So, I fake my eye test.

Faking an eye exam is a delicate balance between naming letters on the chart on a wall incorrectly but not so incorrectly as to get a strong prescription. Since I have little experience in eye charts save the yearly reading of E's and M's on the school nurse's wall, I decide in order to fail the test enough to get glasses so Bob will like me but weak enough so I can still see him, the letters should become blurry one row above the row that is truly blurry. This takes a lot of forethought and can't be planned well since eye charts are not distributed for practice in advance.

The next question becomes how to call the letters incorrectly. After all, an M cannot look like a W, a C can look like an O. In evaluating this, I further decide an O is not likely to become a C. Complicated to be sure, and all this must be figured out and acted upon credibly. I realize few children try to trick a doctor in order to get glasses. I suspect he believes me when I stumble over letters.

"Hmmm," I say with appropriate worry in my voice when examining line six from the top. "I'm not really sure if that is a C or an O." I cannot stray far from my plan. "The next could be a small a or o. I think it is an a," I say, clearly knowing it is an o.

When the eye doctor says in a serious tone, "Are you positive?" I am not sure whether I have gone overboard and have tested myself into Coke-bottle glasses or if he thinks I am illiterate and unable to distinguish the letters of the alphabet. I back off and tell him the correct letter. He breathes a relieved exhale. I get to pick out glasses.

Bob Bennett continues to chase Jane on the playground.

My mother could put together the perfect ensemble for any occasion, from shoes to matching purse. Wherever she went, people commented on her clothes. She rarely paid full price for an outfit. She could find sales or combine pieces she had in her closet and walk out the door feeling comfortable in her appearance.

Her eyeglasses, on the other hand, were always ten years out of fashion. Like many, she started needing glasses for reading and distance as she got older, causing her to wear bi-focals and eventually tri-focals. While many were using "progressive lenses" with no breaks for bifocals, Mom was still fitting her old frames with a new prescription but the same old lines.

When Mom first started showing signs of memory loss, and for ten years following, she had the same, pink-framed glasses that went from the top of her eyebrows to the top of her cheekbones. Given the size, they well could have been the same glasses she wore in the 80s.

The trouble was we could not tell if she needed a new prescription or whether she could see well with her current glasses. Although they often slipped down her nose after she lost weight in her face, she was content to push them back to the bridge of her nose or peer over them. Was she seeing us clearly? We didn't know for sure. Logic would tell us she could not.

After Mom's second seizure, we wondered how much her hesitancy to walk over thresholds or take confident steps stemmed from a change in her disease or if she really couldn't see well. Dad consulted the eye doctor, who said he hadn't changed her prescription in at least eight years and probably hadn't seen her in almost the same length of time. We assumed her eyes had changed. But how could she be tested? She couldn't read anymore, couldn't describe in words a regular E compared with a sideways E. Couldn't even understand any of the normal eye doctor questions they asked with the contraption they placed in front of faces. We were sure the machine would frighten her.

The doctor said he had the same difficulty testing young

children unfamiliar with letters and who were unreliable re-sponders. He offered to test Mom to see what he could dis-cover about her prescription. "Do you see more clearly with this lens or that one?" the doctor asked. No response. Mom sat in the chair for a brief time, fidgeted, pushed away the ma-chine and walked out of the room.

The doctor suggested Dad get three prescription levels of drugstore glasses, the lowest a bit higher than her old pre-scription, assuming at base level that it changed.

"Use your keen observation skills to determine if Shirley can see better or not," the doctor instructed my father.

Dad bought +200, +225 and +250. "I don't know how the heck I'm going to be able to tell," Dad said.

"If she starts bumping into walls, they're not right," I told him.

We started with the middle prescription. She walked fine with them on. She was not feeding herself but could see the utensil coming her way and opened her mouth to eat.

A bonus to the trial was that she looked modern and hip! The *Adam Ant* cartoon glasses were replaced with sleek rimless glasses on the bottom edge and thicker, black metal tops that cleared her eyes but stayed under her brows. Her glasses no longer slipped to the tip of her nose. These fashion-able glasses took away the pale sick look of the pink glasses, framed her eyes, and put some life into them. Mom's whole personality seemed to change.

It was almost as if the glasses were a new medicine we were experimenting with to determine if it improved her quality of life. As far as being able to see faces clearly and focus on her surroundings, the new glasses were a success. We knew Mom could see better because she responded more to visitors with smiles and focused attention. And even though they were just a pair of glasses, our perception of her condition changed.

When we showed her photo albums of family members, her face lit up, especially when she saw pictures of her great-grandchildren. We showed her old photo albums belonging to her parents with pictures slipped into four white corner pieces glued in place on black construction paper pages. She smiled and pointed to the photos of her mother and father as young parents. Black and white photos of my brother and I stuffed into snowsuits brought smiles. In newer albums that I put together were photos of her grandson Tim, taken when he was two years old in 1979. In those pictures of Tim and Mom, a blue version of the pink glasses. Guess it really had been time for a change.

* * *

What works:

- Assuming your loved one might not see well. You won't be able to get a valid exam so ask the doctor to suggest three prescriptions to pick up at the drug store. Try observing if he or she is having new problems seeing pages of books or photo albums up close, then ask the doctor to give options for distance and reading. Keep the distance glasses on most of the time and switch when showing photo albums or other books.
- Finding an understanding optician who will adjust glasses to fit properly. The optician may balk because they are drugstore glasses or because of being afraid of

breaking the glasses. Just assure him or her they will not be held responsible.

11

Passing Away

Journey's End

I am called out of a party by my father.

"Your mother has pneumonia and they have taken her to the hospital. She is in serious condition."

"I'll drive right down."

Dave drops me at my office so I can wrap up loose ends at work. I send him home to pack a bag.

"What should I pack?"

"Oh, the usual, just for a few days. Shirts, pants, underwear, toiletries. Whatever you would pack for yourself."

After the three-and-a-half-hour drive, I meet Dad in Mom's room at the hospital. Her breathing is very labored, rattling. Dad explains she had aspirated some food and her swallowing reflex is failing. She is given medication to diminish the amount of mucus she produces. Still, she wakes up gasping for air, terror in her eyes.

"I'm sleeping here," I tell Dad, pointing to the other hospital bed.

I open my suitcase and laugh out loud. Blue jeans? Check. Night clothes? Check. Toiletries? Check. Shirts? Uncheck. Dave has packed a white blouse — too small but kept in my closet for the day I lose weight and a Christian Dior formal blouse with plunging neckline I bought at Good Will for $5.00 and meant to return. He has packed one shirt I can wear. It doesn't matter. I am suddenly aware of how sometimes I focus on things that do not matter.

In the night, Mom wakes often, struggling to breathe. The nurse continues to give medication to help with her breathing, but she frequently chokes. Each time she gasps for breath, she bolts upright and clutches her throat.

I jump up, speak quietly, "It's all right Mom. Breathe slowly. You'll catch your breath."

She recovers and falls back to sleep, only to gasp again within a half hour.

My brother Eric arrives in the morning and he, Dad and I meet with a doctor called a hospitalist. This is a position we have never heard of. Her entire practice is taking care of patients in the hospital. She keeps all primary physicians aware of their patients' conditions but treats each as her own patient while in the hospital.

"She is nearing the end," the doctor says. The words are direct and delivered with compassion. "We can keep her comfortable here, but she would be more comfortable in familiar surroundings where hospice can do everything we do. We can keep her here or discharge her. What do you want us to do?"

Eric stands behind my father and points down and shakes

his head no. Dad asks us what we think. We say to bring her back to Watson Field, the facility she has lived in for the past two years.

Before we arrive, the staff have readied a new room for her and have taken all her photos and placed them on the windowsill so she can see them from her bed if she wakes. The watercolor of the house she lived in for 40 years hangs on the wall. Her room is a mini version of the home she loves.

Mom sleeps one more night in the hospital, and more peacefully than the night before. I awake early and take a shower. When I walk into the room, Mom is sitting up, eating pudding fed to her by a nurse! She is actually swallowing small amounts. She looks over at me and smiles. Like a cat with nine lives, Mom seems to be recovering.

The doctor explains this happens sometimes and to be cautiously optimistic. If she has another episode of aspiration, it will be much worse, she says. The nurse must be very careful with the amounts of food she gives her.

An ambulance brings Mom to Watson Field. We arrive after she is settled in bed. Eric and I walk over to the side of her bed. She opens her eyes and with a big smile says, "Hi!" She has not spoken in years.

I leave that afternoon, as she seems to be recovering from the pneumonia. Eric stays another day. When he comes into her room with Dad the next morning, Mom's bed is empty. They panic but find her, dressed in khaki pants and a peach sweater, sitting in the day room with other residents. I am happy to hear of her recovery. Eric flies home to Michigan.

Two days later Dad calls to say Mom has aspirated food again. "I don't think you have to rush down. Come tomorrow."

I leave within the hour.

As I sit next to her this morning, Dad is shaving in the bathroom. I tap the keys on my phone to write an email. Partway through writing it, I look at Mom and think, uh-oh, she's not breathing. I stand and hover over her. Her breathing is very shallow with long periods of apnea. But she is still breathing. I sit down and finish the short email, 30 seconds at most, and look again. Mom is not breathing.

I get Dad. "I think she's gone," I tell him.

We cry, hold hands, and say a prayer. I get the hospice nurse. She confirms that Mom has died.

I call my brother. He cries, too. I am happy he saw her recover before he left. The last word she spoke was to Eric and me when she said her big, smiley, "Hi!"

I hold Mom's hand. It is warm. I think, of course it would be. But I have never considered this before, that shortly after someone stops breathing, the blood that has been flowing is still in her veins, keeping her warm. I try to close her mouth – she has been breathing with her mouth gaping open all night — and think with a little chuckle in the middle of the sadness that Mom would not want anyone to see her with her mouth open like that. But it won't close, and it feels disrespectful to force it.

Watson Field has a ritual when someone passes away. The hearse comes to the back door. All the staff who knew Mom assemble in her room. Mom is placed on a stretcher and covered first with a white cloth then with a prayer blanket crocheted by a wonderful lay priest we know. They all walk with her to the funeral vehicle, some on each side of Mom, their hands resting on her. Many of them are crying. "Your mother was a beautiful person," one says. "She was always happy," another adds. "We are going to miss her."

I believe God chooses who is there in our coming in and going out; those of us given the gift to be present are not special, but we are blessed. That I could spend the night holding Mom's hand, be there with her, was one of the greatest gifts. I know her passing was peaceful. I can assure Eric and Dad. There was no last gasp, no struggle. There was silence in the early morning except for water running in the bathroom, giggles down the hallway, the shuffling of slippers outside Mom's door.

I understood the expression, *passed away* for the first time.

12

What Also Worked

- When my mother thought her parents would be worried if she didn't come home, instead of telling her they had passed away, we told her we called her parents and told them she'd be home in the morning. She was relieved versus sad that her parents had died, and she hadn't gone to the funeral.
- Walks were a great activity where we could count things – on the beach we counted gulls, dogs, houses, anything of interest. We collected shells and rocks we liked.
- My mother liked to drink wine, but she didn't remember how many glasses she had and would drink too much. We found non-alcoholic wine, so she could have a drink but not become intoxicated.
- Dad wrote the date and activities on a dry erase board and put it in the kitchen, so Mom would know the date and look forward to events
- At restaurants, instead of Mom feeling embarrassed at

not knowing what to order, Dad would order and then say, "You like chicken piccata, right?" then Mom would know what to choose.

- Mom called the police because there was a strange man in her house, my father, whom she locked out. The police put a note in their records, so they would know she had Alzheimer's.

- We had an alarm in our home, and Dad set it to go off when a door was opened from the inside. Prior to setting the alarm, Mom wandered from our house in the middle of the night.

- Dad insisted her memory unit work to duplicate those habits that were familiar – he brought cloth napkins for meals. Mom always wore lipstick and he asked the staff to put lipstick on her. Her outfits always matched.

- Dad brought her dogs to visit. While she didn't recognize them as her dogs, she enjoyed their company. So did the other residents.

- Friends felt a visit was irrelevant because Mom "wouldn't know their name." Dad explained that we have moments in life that make us happy with people whose names we don't know. He called all her close friends and suggested they visit just to make my mother happy.

- Mom's room had photos of all her loved ones. We put stickers on the frames with names of those in the photos.

- We made photo books online and looked through them for hours. Old photos from her parents' books were especially enjoyable, and we talked about each of the people.

Acknowledgements

Many people supported this book and also supported my family through Mom's Alzheimer's Disease. In our writing group, Marcia Reese and Pam Tallmadge encouraged me and my writing for more than 15 years. This means they were a part of my mother's decline into this horrible disease and grieved for me when my mother passed away. They critiqued, edited, and offered important insights to these stories.

Thanks to Lesley Kellas Payne, editor extraordinaire, who helped format the stories, clarify the words, and added necessary grammatical insights and punctuation. Thanks to author J. Alison James who ignited the spark that started this writing journey.

Nancy Euchner, RN of New Hampshire, was my mother's Care Coordinator who helped and guided our family during changes in Mom's disease. Thanks to Kelly Jennings who worked for my family for 40 years and is like another daughter to my parents; to Karin Finnegan who was respite for my father and through her patience and humor gave Mom social company.

A special thanks to my husband, Dave, who patiently supported our family, sometimes from the sidelines and sometimes in the trenches. Thanks to my brother, Eric, my teammate on this journey. Most importantly, thanks to my father who was the genius behind all the techniques that helped my mother live with grace, surrounded by love.

CPSIA information can be obtained
at www.ICGtesting.com
Printed in the USA
BVHW031438210621
610124BV00005B/1101